Sport Answers Back!

by Lola Francis
illustrated by Brandon Reese

Harcourt
SCHOOL PUBLISHERS

Printed in China

ISBN 10: 0-15-351500-7
ISBN 13: 978-0-15-351500-2

Ordering Options
ISBN 10: 0-15-351213-X (Grade 3 Advanced Collection)
ISBN 13: 978-0-15-351213-1 (Grade 3 Advanced Collection)
ISBN 10: 0-15-358090-9 (package of 5)
ISBN 13: 978-0-15-358090-1 (package of 5)

4 5 6 7 8 9 10 0940 12 11 10 09

Characters

Stacy   Aimee   Matt

Carlos   Noah   Madeleine

Setting: The offices of *Sport Kid* magazine

Stacy: All right, is everyone here? We need to work on the new advice section for the next issue of the magazine.

Aimee: It's hard to decide which topics to choose—all the questions are so interesting!

Stacy: Well, no matter which ones we choose, let's just make sure that the advice is sensible and encouraging. Now no more dodging our work, let's get started. Matt, I heard you rustling through the letters and e-mails this morning. I'm sure you must have found something worthwhile. Do you want to go first?

Matt: I suppose I will. This is a brief but very important question:

Dear *Sport Kid*:

Sometimes I get tired and slow down toward the end of a game. What should I eat before a game to give me enough energy to play my best?

Sincerely,

Worn Out

Carlos: There are so many types of snacks available. It's hard to know which one will make you feel your best.

Stacy: Matt, you're the nutrition editor. What will help our tired friend?

Matt: Here's what I wrote:

Dear Worn Out,

    The food you eat can really affect your game! Stay away from snacks that have a lot of sugar and caffeine. These will give you a quick burst of energy, but they burn off quickly. Fresh or dried fruit and nuts are easy, healthy snacks that will give you enough energy to be at your best for a whole game.

    Also, don't forget to drink enough water, especially on hot days!

Matt

Sport Kid Health Editor

Noah: That's great advice, Matt. Soon "Worn Out" won't be worn out anymore!

Stacy: I agree. Thanks, Matt. Madeleine, I caught a glimpse of you looking at some letters this morning. Did you find something?

Madeleine: Absolutely—here's a super question:

Dear *Sport Kid*:

I love playing sports, but I think I could be even better if I could get stronger and faster. Should I start to lift weights? Should I run sprints? What can I do to improve myself?

Your loyal reader,
Future Star

Stacy: What do you think, Madeleine?

Madeleine: This is what I wrote:

Dear Future Star,

I think it's fantastic that you want to improve yourself! Kids' bodies can get stronger just by being active—that means running and playing a lot. Stretching will also help because it will keep your body flexible and can protect you from some injuries.

The best way for you to devise a workout program is to consult your coaches and your doctor. They'll recommend the right exercises for you!

Madeleine

Sport Kid Fitness Editor

Carlos: That's good advice, Madeleine. Listen to this:

Dear Sport Kid,

I love to play basketball, but I'm not enjoying playing in my town league. It seems like I only play five minutes a game—and that's after everyone else has gotten into the game. How can I get my coach to give me more time so I can show my skills?

Yours truly,

Last One on the Bench

Aimee: Being left on the bench feels just awful. One time I sobbed so much on the way home from a game that my brother complained about the horrific din I was making.

Carlos: It's a bothersome problem. How does this answer sound?

Dear Last,

Talk to your coach about how you feel. Ask him or her about what you need to improve on, and then work hard on those things in practice. You'll undoubtedly impress your coach, and soon you'll increase your minutes, too!

Carlos

Sport Kid Team Player Editor

Stacy: That's a good answer, Carlos. I hope "Last" takes your advice!

Aimee: I found a really good question. Here you go:

Dear *Sport Kid*,

   I play soccer, hockey, baseball, and I'm on the swim team. I'm hoping to learn to play tennis and golf, too. I love all my sports and my teams, but some people are telling me that I can only be really good if I pick one and concentrate on that. I'd hate to give any up. What do you think?

Sincerely yours,
All Sports

Matt: That's one busy kid! What do you think, Aimee?

Aimee: Here's what I wrote:

Dear All Sports,

    Some people think it's better to devote all your time to one sport, but I think it's better to play a variety. The skills you use in one sport can often help you in another! Read about some of today's biggest star athletes—you'll see that they played several sports when they were young.

                    Aimee

                    Sport Kid Sport Choice Consultant

Stacy: I agree with you, Aimee. Playing basketball has made my feet quicker for soccer.

Aimee: It's a very important issue for many kids. I hope "All Sports" just plays to have fun.

Stacy: Noah, did you find any questions you liked?

Noah: I sure did! Listen to this:

Dear *Sport Kid*,

I'm the smallest one on all my teams. It seems like everyone is growing faster than I am. I'm a good athlete, but no one notices me because I'm small. What can I do? How can I grow more?

Yours truly,

Too Small

Carlos: That's a tough question!

Noah: I agree. Here's my response:

Dear Too Small,

Don't worry about being small. Not everyone grows at the same speed. Just because you're small now doesn't mean that you'll never catch up. Many people have growth spurts in their teens, so don't give up! Just keep practicing and playing. No matter how small you are, people will notice someone who plays hard and plays right.

Hang in there,

Noah

Sport Kid Health Editor

Stacy: I think that's a really thoughtful answer, Noah. I hope "Too Small" reads it and feels better.

Madeleine: There are still a lot of questions here, Stacy. Do we have room for more?

Stacy: Unfortunately, I think that fills up all the space on our advice page. However, it's good to know that we have plenty of choices for our next issue.

Matt: I already have some picked out.

Aimee: So do I!

Stacy: That's great—but let's finish this issue first!

Think Critically

1. What is the main idea of this Readers' Theater?

2. What is the author's purpose for writing this Readers' Theater?

3. What does "Future Star" want to learn about?

4. What advice does Carlos give "Last One on the Bench"?

5. Would you ask these kids for advice about sports? Why or why not?

 Social Studies

Sports History Choose a sport. Look up information about when and how it was first played. Also find out about some important figures in its history. Use the information to write a magazine article about the sport.

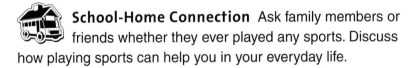 **School-Home Connection** Ask family members or friends whether they ever played any sports. Discuss how playing sports can help you in your everyday life.

Word Count: 1,027